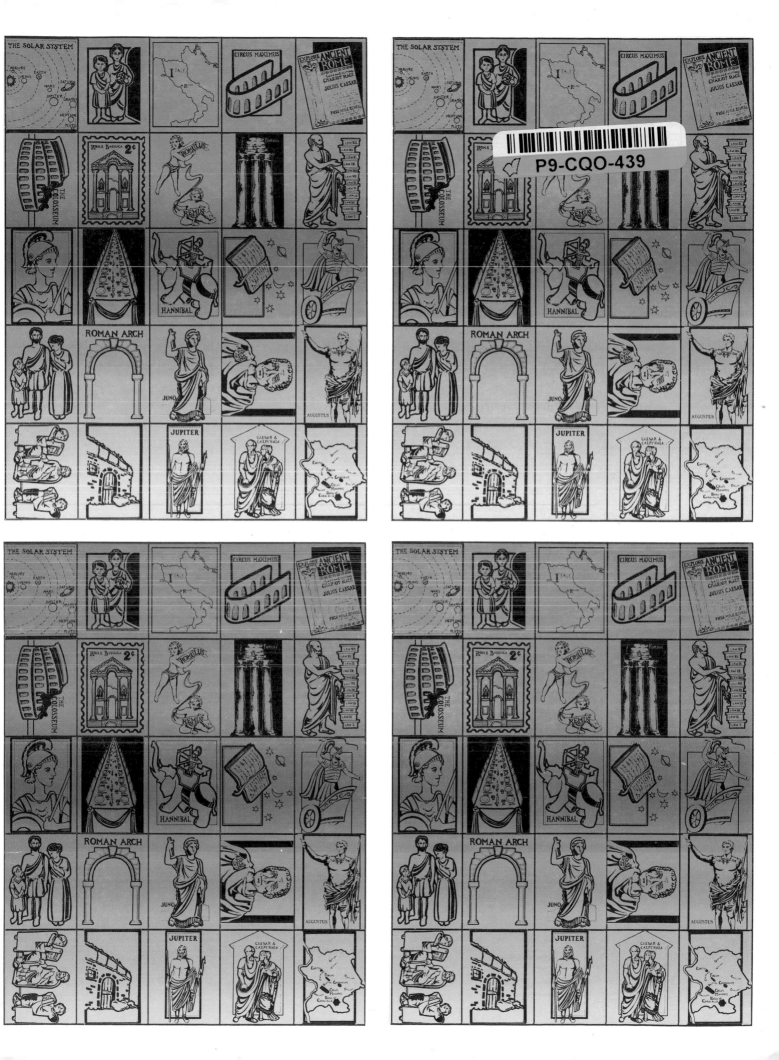

ANCIENT CIVILIZATIONS
ROME

By
Jane Pofahl

Illustrated By
Julie Anderson

Cover Illustration By
Mark Anthony

Publishers
T.S. Denison & Company, Inc.
Minneapolis, Minnesota 55431

T.S. Denison and Company, Inc.

Standard Book Number: 513-02189-2
Ancient Civilizations—Rome
Copyright © 1993 by T.S. Denison & Co., Inc.
9601 Newton Avenue South
Minneapolis, Minnesota 55431

Introduction

History is the living record of the human race—exciting as it is varied. *The Time Traveler Series* will aid you as you teach the colorful history of ancient civilizations to your children and explore such topics as the development of language, early government, ancient cultures and art forms, scientific discoveries, and the historic personalities who helped shape our own present-day culture.

After each topic is presented, activity pages are provided for your children to implement suggested vocabulary, conduct further research, and provide creative answers/solutions to historical situations. Fun reproducible pages are also included to review the historical and cultural facts studied on the preceding pages.

Each book contains the following:

- topic information pages
- research/activity pages (including maps, charts, research topics, and creative thinking activities)
- reproducible activity pages
- time period stickers

The Time Traveler Series was created to spark the intrigue of your children and lay a foundation for enjoyable history instruction and learning. Have fun!

Table of Contents

A Historical Overview of Rome

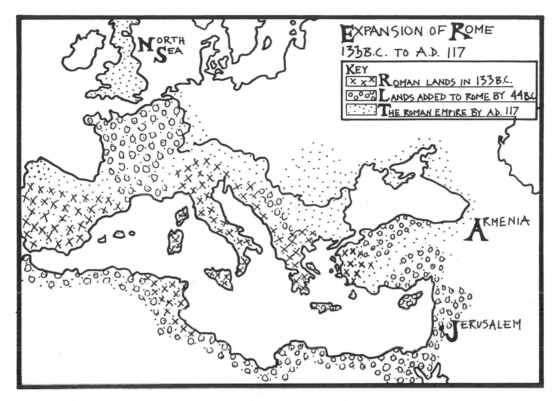

Ancient Rome was located on the Tiber River in Italy, exactly where Rome, Italy, now stands today. It was a city, but at the height of the Roman Empire, it also controlled the countries of England, Spain, France, Germany, Iran, Iraq, Syria, Greece, Israel, Egypt, and parts of Africa and Asia.

The Alps Mountains to the north, the Appenine Mountains to the east, as well as the Mediterranean Sea to the west protected Rome from invaders. The people living along the Tiber River were the Latins, who were conquered around 600 B.C. by the Etruscans. In 509 B.C. the Romans drove out the Etruscans and claimed the land as their own.

Ancient Roman history can be divided into two main time periods: the **Roman Republic**, dating from 509 B.C. to 44 B.C.; and the **Roman Empire**, dating from 44 B.C. to A.D. 455. During the Republic, Romans set up a system of government where two consuls served a one-year term and were advised by the members of the Senate, a powerful decision-making body made up exclusively of wealthy patricians. All male citizens serving in the army were members of the Assembly. The rest of the Roman population were either poor plebeians or slaves. Only 10 percent of the population in Rome were patricians, while the plebeians and slaves comprised the other 90 percent. The plebeians revolted against the powerful patricians, and civil war broke out for nearly one hundred years. A general named Julius Caesar took control of the government in 49 B.C. Caesar brought stability to Rome, but his enemies feared he would make himself king, so they killed him in 44 B.C. This led to more fighting over the control of Rome, and the Republic ended.

AUGUSTUS

In 27 B.C., Julius Caesar's great-nephew, Augustus, became the first ruler of the Roman Empire. This was the beginning of the Pax Romana, or Roman peace. Augustus added many provinces to the Empire at this time. Roads, buildings, bridges, and aqueducts were built to connect the lands conquered by Rome. The Empire became too large to control, and in A.D. 352 it was divided into the Eastern and Western Empires. Invaders were constantly breaking down Rome's empire, which ended in A.D. 455 when Vandals from the north raided Rome.

Geography

Italy is a boot-shaped country and forms a peninsula into the Mediterranean Sea. Ancient Rome was a city surrounded by seven hills, located along the Tiber River in central Italy. The Tiber River provided a waterway to the Mediterranean Sea.

Natural barriers helped protect Rome from its enemies for many years. The Alps Mountains to the north and the Apennine Mountains to the east, running the length of Italy, provided protection. Rome was located inland about fifteen miles and controlled the Tiber River, so it could not be easily attacked by sea. The seven steep hills that ringed around the city made it difficult for enemies to spring a surprise raid on Rome. (However, during the Punic Wars, fought between Rome and Carthage between 264 and 146 B.C., a brilliant Carthaginian general named Hannibal attacked Rome by crossing the Alps on elephants.)

The northwest and central sections of Italy are rough and mountainous. The southern part is more level and fertile and was used for farming.

The eastern coastline of Italy has few good harbors. Most of the harbors used by ancient Romans to trade goods with other parts of the Roman Empire lay on the western coast of the country.

Italy's mild climate was attractive to ancient settlers. Temperatures rarely dip below 60° F (15° C) or above 85° F (29° C). Rainfall amounts to about thirty inches (76 cm) per year.

Geography

RESEARCH QUESTIONS

1. In a dictionary, find the following words: *peninsula, surround, waterway, barrier, protection, inland, raid, brilliant, fertile, harbor,* and *settler.* Define each word and use it in a sentence.

2. In an encyclopedia or a world atlas, find out the average temperature by month for Rome. How would knowing each month's temperature help the Romans? Make a chart of Rome's monthly temperatures and report your findings to the group.

PROJECTS

1. You are an ancient Latin who has settled in the western part of Italy on a flat plain south of the Tiber River. What kinds of foods do you eat? Find out and draw a picture illustrating your findings. (Remember to label the foods.)

2. Where would you want to live in ancient Italy if you were a farmer? A sailor? A senator? A shepherd? A merchant?

3. Would you feel safe from invaders in ancient Rome? Why or why not?

4. The city of Rome was named after a myth about twin brothers, *Romulus* and *Remus.* Find out more about this myth and draw a picture of it.

Expansion of Rome 133 B.C. to A.D. 117

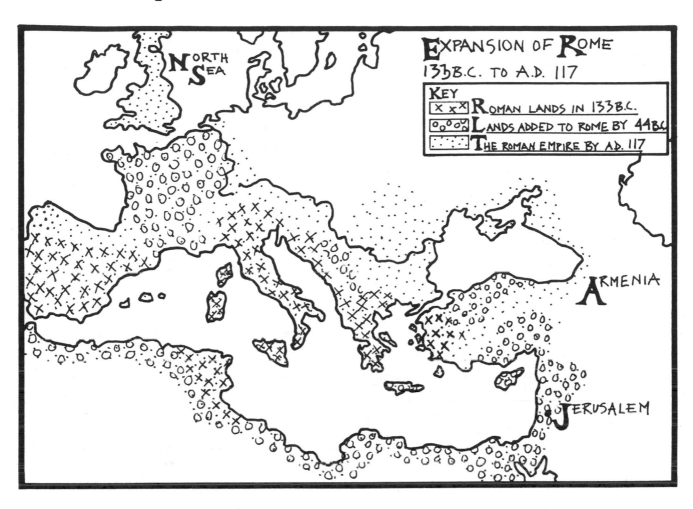

1. Identify the following on your map (refer to a map of the Roman Empire in an encyclopedia):
   - Rome
   - Mediterranean Sea
   - Adriatic Sea
   - Corsica
   - Atlantic Ocean
   - Tiber River
   - Alps Mountains
   - Apennines Mountains
   - Carthage (in Africa)
   - Britain
   - Sardinia
   - Gaul (now France)
   - Sicily
   - Iberia (now Spain)

2. Make a compass in the lower left corner of your map. Label the directions.

3. Shade the water blue and the mountain ranges grey. Outline all the lands included in the Roman Empire by A.D. 117 in purple.

4. How did Hannibal attack Rome? _____
   _____

5. The harbors on Italy's western coast made it easy to trade with other countries. How did trade with other Mediterranean people help the early Romans?
   _____
   _____

The Roman Republic

The earliest rulers of Rome were the Etruscans, a fierce tribe who controlled the Latins for about one hundred years. After the Etruscan rule ended, the Romans set up a form of government called a republic. In this system the people elect their own leaders.

The government in Rome was headed by two consuls who explained and carried out the laws. They were chosen for a one-year term by the Assembly of Centuries. All male citizens who had served in the army were members of the Assembly, and they elected the government officials. The most powerful group in government was the Senate. This group was made up of former consuls and anyone else the consuls chose. All senators were patricians, or upper-class Romans.

In time, the plebeians, or lower-class workers, gained more power in the government. Around 494 B.C., they elected tribunes to speak up for them in the Senate and protect their interests. The plebeians also wanted the laws of Rome written down so that everyone would know their rights. In 450 B.C., the laws were carved on bronze tablets, known as the Twelve Tables, and were placed in the Forum.

A struggle for power in Rome between the Senate and the plebeians led to almost one hundred years of civil war. The fighting ended when Julius Caesar became dictator, but after his death in 44 B.C. the Roman Republic ended.

The Roman Republic

RESEARCH QUESTIONS

1. In a dictionary, find the following words: *fierce, government, republic, elect, consul, citizen, former, patrician, plebeian, tribune, tablet,* and *civil war.* Define each word and use it in a sentence.

2. Make a flow chart of the government during the Roman Republic. Show the most powerful group at the top, the next most powerful under it, and so on, to the bottom of the chart.

3. Find out about the *Punic Wars* that Rome fought with Carthage during the Republic. Then imagine that you are the Carthaginian general, Hannibal, and explain your battle plan.

HANNIBAL

PROJECTS

1. Write or discuss: What would be the most difficult part of a tribune's job?

2. Direct twelve cooperative learning groups to each decide on one law that would be fair for all Romans. Then take twelve shoe boxes and cover them with white paper. Each group writes their law on an upright shoe box (make sure no two laws are the same) and displays it. Vote on which laws the class feels are "fair."

3. If you were a consul (and you knew that next year you would be in the Senate), would you vote against the Senate's wishes? Why or why not?

Julius Caesar

One of the greatest rulers of Rome was Julius Caesar, who was born into a patrician family around 100 B.C. As a boy, Gaius Julius Caesar studied Latin and Greek grammar, literature, math, music, and astronomy. When he was fourteen, Caesar studied rhetoric, which is the ability to speak in public and persuade listeners to your way of thinking.

In 58 B.C., Caesar led an army that conquered Gaul, now known as France. In 49 B.C., the Senate in Rome became afraid of Caesar's power and popularity with the common people. The Senate ordered him to return to Rome without his army. Instead, Caesar marched his army into Rome and seized control of the government himself. The people made him "Dictator for Life."

As Rome's ruler, Caesar made many improvements. He put honest men in government positions. He made taxes fairer and gave land to the poor. He also improved the calendar into what was named the Julian Calendar—a calendar used throughout the world for over fifteen hundred years.

Many senators felt Caesar was disrespectful toward them and that he was wrong to take the title of dictator. They feared he wanted to make himself king. On March 15, 44 B.C., Julius Caesar was stabbed to death in the Forum by his friend Brutus, who had been conspiring with twenty senators.

Julius Caesar

RESEARCH QUESTIONS

1. In a dictionary, find the following words: *grammar, literature, astronomy, rhetoric, persuade, conquer, popularity, seize, dictator, disrespectful* and *conspire*. Define each word and use it in a sentence.

2. The name *Caesar* has been used throughout history as a title for a ruler, such as *Czar* in Russia and *Kaiser* in Germany. Find out about at least one famous czar and kaiser and share your findings with the group.

PROJECTS

1. Caesar's wife, Calpurnia, dreamed she heard the words, "Beware the Ides of March!" (*ides* means "middle"). Caesar ignored her warning and was killed on the Ides of March. Write about a time you had a hunch that came true.

2. Brainstorm and list all the options Brutus and the senators could have considered besides killing Caesar.

3. You are Julius Caesar. The Senate has ordered you to come back to Rome alone. You know that:
   - if you go alone, you might be a war hero.
   - if you go alone, the Senate might imprison you.
   - if you go with your army and win, you could rule the city.
   - if you go with your army and loose, you could also loose your life.

   What will you do? Explain why.

CAESAR & CALPURNIA

The Caesar Cipher

Did you know that Julius Caesar invented a famous code? When he was a general, he needed to send coded messages to his men in battle. He used many complex codes in case one of his messages fell into enemy hands, but his most famous cipher is easy to read—once you know the trick! It's called a shift code, and it works like this:

1. Write all the letters of the alphabet in order.

2. Underneath it, shift the beginning letter A over however many places you want. Caesar shifted three letters, so A became D, B became E, and so on to the end of the alphabet.

Regular

A B C D E F G H I J K L M N O P Q R S T U V W X Y Z

Cipher

D E F G H I J K L M N O P Q R S T U V W X Y Z A B C

Decipher the following messages.

FDQ BRX UHDG WKLV FRGH ?

_____

L WKLQN BRX FDQ !

_____

Write your own message in code and see if a friend can decipher it.

_____

The Roman Empire

After Julius Caesar's death in 44 B.C., many men vied for control of Rome. The winner was Julius Caesar's great-nephew and adopted son, Octavian. The Senate gave him the title of Augustus, and he became the sole leader of Rome.

Augustus governed Rome for more than forty years, from 27 B.C. to A.D. 14. He used his power to stabilize the government of Rome, add many new provinces to the Empire, and rebuild the city of Rome after one hundred years of civil war.

The time between 27 B.C. and A.D. 200 is called the Pax Romana, or Roman peace. For almost two hundred years Rome did not fight any major wars. The Romans concentrated their efforts on building roads and aqueducts and reconstructing the buildings in the Forum. To keep the people amused, the Romans built huge amphitheaters, such as the Colosseum, where gladiators would fight each other in hand-to-hand combat. Sometimes the floor of the Colosseum was flooded so that mock naval battles could be presented. Romans also enjoyed watching chariot races in the Circus Maximus.

The Roman Empire came to an end because it was too large to control. In A.D. 395, it was split into the Western Empire (based in Rome) and the Eastern Empire (based in Constantinople, Turkey). In A.D. 455, barbarians destroyed Rome, and the Roman Empire ended.

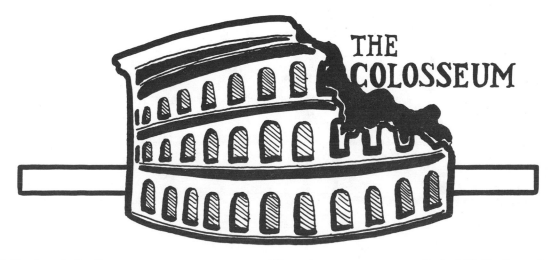

THE COLOSSEUM

The Roman Empire

RESEARCH QUESTIONS

1. In a dictionary, find the following words: *vie, sole, stabilize, province, concentrate, aqueduct, reconstruct, amuse, amphitheater, gladiator, combat, mock, naval, chariot,* and *barbarian.* Define each word and use it in a sentence.

2. Draw a map of the Roman Empire and all of its *provinces*, or conquered countries.

3. Make a timeline of ancient Rome. (Be careful—Rome began in the time of B.C. and reached its height in A.D. time.) At the bottom of your chart, explain the meanings of *B.C.* and *A.D.*

4. Find out more about the Eastern Roman Empire. Why was it also called the *Byzantine Empire*? Who was *Justinian* and why was he famous? Report your findings to the group.

PROJECTS

1. Make a model of the Colosseum. Explain where the gladiators and wild animals were kept before combat and how the arena was flooded for naval battles.

2. Make a diagram of the Circus Maximus. Show how the chariot races were set up and run.

3. Design and draw an authentic gladiator uniform. Be creative.

Roman Empire Crossword

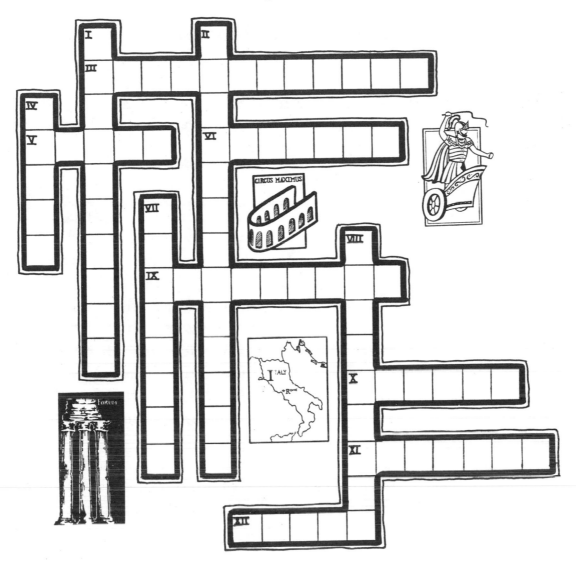

ACROSS:

III A huge open-air arena in which contests were held.
V River which flows through Rome.
VI Two-wheeled cart pulled by horses.
IX A man forced to fight other men in hand-to-hand combat.
X Gave Octavian the title of Augustus.
XI Ruler of an empire.
XII Center of Rome which contained buildings, temples, and shops.

DOWN:

I Invaders who destroyed Rome in A.D. 455.
II Arena where chariot races were held.
IV Boot-shaped; Rome is located in it.
VII First emperor of the Roman Empire.
VIII Most famous amphitheater where gladiator fights occurred.

Daily Life of Plebeians

Ninety percent of the people living in ancient Rome did not belong to the wealthy patrician class. These were the plebeians, or working class of Rome, as well as soldiers and slaves.

Plebeians were workers, farmers, and shopkeepers. They could not hold important government offices or marry into the patrician class. Since they did not own land, they were not citizens and could not vote in the Senate until tribunes were elected to represent them in 494 B.C.

Life for plebeians was not easy. Up at dawn, the entire family ate a meager breakfast of bread and water and then went to work in the shop or fields. Only the wealthy could afford to educate their children, so plebeian boys learned a trade from their fathers and girls learned household skills from their mothers. They worked until mid-afternoon and went home to a simple meal of wheat porridge with vegetables or fruits.

Plebeians lived in crowded tenements, or apartments, above shops in the city. Entire families were forced to live in one room, with no privacy or running water. Fire was a constant danger because so many people lived and cooked their foods in such crowded quarters.

Daily Life of Plebeians

RESEARCH QUESTIONS

1. In a dictionary, find the following words: *represent, meager, educate, porridge, tenement, privacy, constant* and *quarters*. Define each word and use it in a sentence.

2. Find out about Rome's "middle class"—the Roman Army. What weapons did they use? What was a *legion*? Why was the *Praetorian Guard* important?

3. Find out what plebeian clothing looked like. Make a plebeian's costume for a doll and explain it.

PROJECTS

1. You are a soldier in the Roman Army. (You can write because your parents saved enough money to send you to school.) Write about a typical day in your journal.

2. Find a description of the plebeian's porridge. Make it and taste it.

3. You are a plebeian child. Where do you live—in the city or in the country? What does your home look like? Do you feel safe in your home? What kind of work does your family do? What do you dream will happen for you in the future? Write a short story about your life.

A Day in the Life of a Plebeian Family

Young Paulo and his sister, Penelope, are plebeians in ancient Rome. They live in a tenement apartment house in the city along with many other families who also had to give up their farms and find work closer to Rome. Here is a typical day for Paulo and his family, but the sentences are out of order. Number the sentences correctly and find out what a day in the life of a plebeian family was like.

_____ In the middle of the afternoon, Paulo and his father headed for home.

_____ When Paulo and his father left for work, Penelope cleared the table.

_____ In the evening, the family relaxed together while Father told stories about the Roman gods and goddesses.

_____ After she had cleared the table, Penelope helped her mother shop for food in the Forum.

PAULO & PENELOPE

_____ Paulo woke up at dawn.

_____ As soon as Paulo and his father arrived, Mother served wheat porridge and turnips for supper.

_____ The entire family ate a bread and water breakfast.

_____ At noon, Paulo took a break from hoeing and ate a crust of bread.

_____ After breakfast, Paulo and his father worked in the fields of Rome.

Daily Life of Patricians

The patricians were the upper class of ancient Rome. They made up only 10 percent of the population, but they were the most powerful people in Rome. Patricians owned much land and belonged to the oldest families of the city.

Rome was a male-dominated society. The father was the head of the family and was called the *pater familias*. A typical day for a male patrician would involve business in the morning; the public baths in the late morning for exercise, a massage, and the latest news; and home to his luxurious villa for the main meal of the day, which started between two and three in the afternoon and lasted for four hours.

A patrician woman was expected to be efficient and dignified. She usually had little schooling and was in charge of the servants. Her days were spent with servants dressing her and arranging her elaborate hairstyle; preparing the day's menu and shopping list for the slaves; overseeing the children; and performing as a gracious hostess for the evening meal.

Both patrician boys and girls were sent to school to learn to read and write Latin from ages five to twelve. After that, girls were taught at home to run a household, and boys were taught literature, history, math, geometry, and astronomy.

Daily Life of Patricians

RESEARCH QUESTIONS

1. In a dictionary, find the following words: *population, dominate, typical, massage, luxurious, villa, efficient, dignified, elaborate, gracious, hostess,* and *geometry.* Define each word and use it in a sentence.

2. Find out about patrician clothing and hairstyles. Draw costume sketches for a man, a woman, a boy, and a girl.

3. Plan the food and entertainment for a Roman banquet. Remember, the meal has to last for four hours!

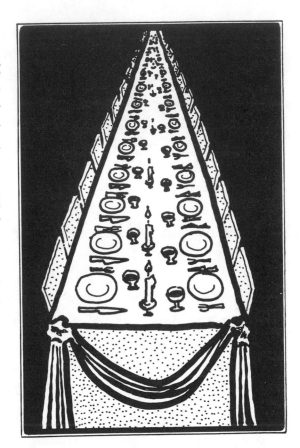

PROJECTS

1. Did patrician women have many rights in Rome? Find out and then write a poem about women's rights in Rome. Use rhythm instruments to chant your poem.

2. Find out what kind of toys patrician children had. Make one.

3. Make a model of a Roman villa. Inside a box, create Roman-style walls using cardboard partitions. Include Roman-style furniture. If possible, add dolls dressed in togas.

Please Pass the Wild Boar!

You are an artist in ancient Rome. You have received a very strange request. You were summoned to the villa of Marcus Portlius this evening, not to draw his portrait, but to draw the foods on his table before his guests arrive! Marcus Portlius is heavily into food (the man is huge) and he wants to remember this evening by the foods that were served. Since Marcus is a big tipper, you don't want to forget the platters of wild boar and peacock, the platter of fruits, the bowl of figs, the baskets of breads, the plate of cheeses, the wine jug, and anything else you see.

Gods and Goddesses

The ancient Romans believed there were many gods and goddesses who had power over all aspects of life. As time went on, the Greek gods appealed to the Romans, and several Greek deities were given Roman names and temples of worship.

The government controlled the religion in ancient Rome. Priests were elected or appointed by government officials. Religious leaders performed public ceremonies to please the gods and goddesses. A few temples were tended by priestesses, such as the Temple of Vesta. Women called Vestal Virgins guarded the holy flame of the goddess, Vestal, and were highly respected in Rome.

Jupiter was the supreme god who governed the sky and the weather. Juno, Jupiter's wife, was a special goddess for women. Mars was the god of farmers and war. Vulcan was the fire-god, Saturn was the wine-god, and Mercury was the messenger of the gods.

When an emperor died, the Romans believed he became a god. This was important because they thought only gods could have eternal life. The Romans believed that the rest of the dead went to live in the underworld.

Gods and Goddesses

RESEARCH QUESTIONS

1. In a dictionary, find the following words: *aspect, deity, temple, worship, appoint, ceremony, tend, respected, supreme, govern, messenger, emperor,* and *underworld*. Define each word and use it in a sentence.

2. Many of the planets are named after Roman gods. Make a chart of the solar system. Label each planet. Identify which ones were named for Roman gods (*example*: Jupiter, ruler of the gods).

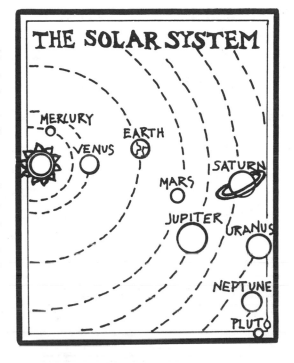

PROJECTS

1. It was a great honor to be chosen as a Vestal Virgin. Find out more about Vestal Virgins. Present a puppet show entitled "A Day in the Life of a Vestal Virgin."

2. The Romans were superstitious and believed in magic, which they thought was performed only by the gods. Learn at least one magic trick and perform it for the group.

3. The month of June was named for Juno, Jupiter's wife who looked after women—even today June is the most popular month for weddings. List other months named for Roman gods and goddesses.

The Forum

If you wanted to know what was going on in ancient Rome, the Forum was the place to find out. Similar to the agora in Greece, the Forum was the main business center of Rome. In addition, temples dedicated to emperors and gods, the Senate building, the Hall of Records, and the open-air marketplace were located in the Forum.

Within the city of Rome, the Forum was found east of the capitol, north of the Circus Maximus, and northwest of the Colosseum. It was in the center of the Seven Hills of Rome. On the highest summit of the city, the Romans built a temple to the supreme god, Jupiter. Leading from the Temple of Jupiter was the Sacra Via, or Sacred Way, which was the main thoroughfare running through the Forum. It wound around past the

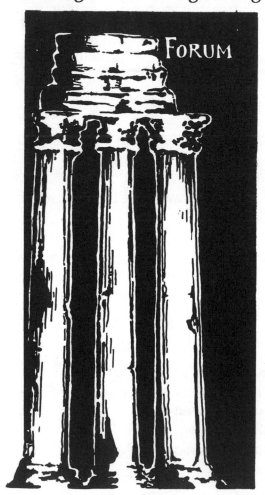

Temple of Saturn, past the Speaker's Platform, through the marketplace, and between the Temple of Castor and Pollux and the Temple of Julius Caesar. Every Roman city had a forum, but the original Forum was in Rome.

The remains of the Forum still exist today in Rome. Three columns from the Temple of Castor and Pollux, a wall from the Temple of Vesta, and the Arch of Titus are still standing amid the rubble.

The Forum

RESEARCH QUESTIONS

1. In a dictionary, find the following words: *similar, agora, dedicate, summit, thoroughfare, platform, original, remains, column, amid,* and *rubble.* Define each word and use it in a sentence.

2. There was a major temple in the Forum dedicated to *Castor* and *Pollux.* Find out the Roman myth about them and draw a picture from the story.

3. Make a picture map of the ancient city of Rome. Locate and label *the Forum, the Colosseum, the Baths of Caracalla, the Circus Maximus, the Capitol, the Tiber River,* and *the Seven Hills of Rome.* (Label each hill by name.)

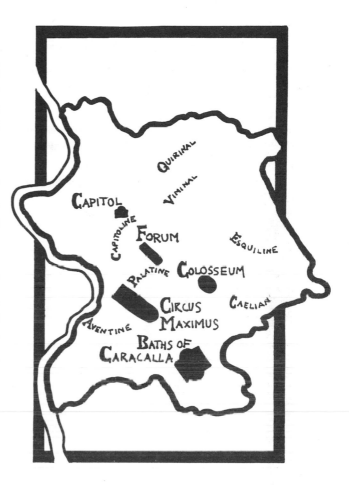

PROJECTS

1. Make a diorama of the Forum. Include the major buildings and place them in their correct locations.

2. Design a stamp for your favorite building in the Forum. Find a picture of it, then draw and color your own picture of it on a white 8 1/2" x 11" sheet of paper. On a separate sheet of paper, write at least five facts you found out about the building.

Name that Temple

You have been selected to name and design the newest temple in the Forum. You may choose to look in books at other temples for design ideas. In the space below:

1. Write the name of the new temple at the top.
2. Draw what the temple looks like from the outside.
3. Write at least two sentences about the temple, such as for whom it was built and why.

Achievements

The ancient Romans were famous for their construction abilities. Bridges, arches, roads, buildings, aqueducts—the Romans built them all! Once the Romans invented concrete by mixing gravel, sand, and crushed limestone, they just kept on building. Soldiers and merchants needed roads to travel throughout the vast Roman Empire safely and quickly. As soon as Roman soldiers conquered another country, the soldiers built more roads. The Appian Way, a famous road built by the Roman soldiers, is still in use today. To travel over water, Romans built bridges. To carry water to all parts of the Empire, they built aqueducts. To honor the Roman gods in the newly conquered lands, they built temples of marble and created arches over the doorways.

The Romans also invented the Latin language. Some people say that Latin is a dead language, but you speak Latin words every day because the English language came from Latin!

We use Roman numerals today in clock faces, outlines, beginning pages in books, and copyright dates. We borrowed these numbers, as well as our present calendar, from the Romans.

Many great writers were ancient Romans. People today study the writings of Julius Caesar, Cicero, and Livi, to name a few.

Achievements

RESEARCH QUESTIONS

1. In a dictionary, find the following words: *construction, ability, arch, concrete, gravel, limestone, merchant, vast,* and *marble.* Define each word and use it in a sentence.

2. Find a list of words in English that were derived from Latin. Make a chart of English words with their Latin roots.

3. Find out more about the Roman arch. Draw a diagram of the arch and write a short report about how the Romans constructed it.

ROMAN ARCH

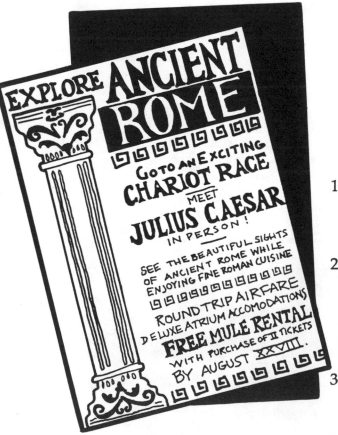

PROJECTS

1. "All roads lead to Rome" is a famous Latin saying. In A.D. 117, why was this a true statement?

2. Imagine you work for a travel agency that can travel back in time. Design a travel poster for ancient Rome, illustrating a great achievement by the Romans.

3. Find out what numbers the Roman numerals I, V, X, C, and M stand for. Invent your own number system.

Roman Achievements Word Search

```
S  S  A  U  B  I  A  S  N  U  Y  K  L  R  V  F  H  W
F  Y  H  A  U  Y  N  I  K  T  U  D  A  Z  V  N  H  E
C  O  N  Q  U  E  R  Q  M  P  O  W  T  N  O  L  D  A
Q  J  K  U  T  F  D  Q  V  X  S  U  I  H  P  I  N  S
H  Q  M  E  P  O  K  C  I  L  C  O  N  C  R  E  T  E
N  F  O  D  Q  X  T  A  T  G  F  R  U  X  W  T  X  C
P  Q  R  U  O  R  M  E  Q  K  F  A  M  D  C  H  S  K
T  L  U  C  O  L  O  S  S  E  U  M  E  F  C  A  Q  K
Y  I  U  T  I  N  Z  A  C  Z  J  P  R  H  Q  H  M  W
I  V  S  S  B  S  L  R  P  M  C  H  A  R  I  O  T  M
C  I  C  E  R  O  A  D  S  B  U  I  L  D  I  N  G  S
E  A  P  P  I  A  N  X  C  H  P  T  S  K  M  V  V  P
W  K  Z  X  D  U  K  Y  A  R  C  H  E  S  R  H  J  Z
I  P  I  X  G  L  S  O  L  D  I  E  R  S  N  K  H  V
V  B  T  T  E  M  P  L  E  S  L  A  L  R  D  M  G  Q
O  B  X  V  S  X  M  R  N  L  F  T  C  B  C  C  L  B
L  I  W  P  O  X  L  Q  D  B  A  E  E  Z  M  Z  T  G
R  C  X  S  H  R  I  F  A  F  O  R  U  M  I  P  P  G
M  U  S  Y  V  G  A  F  R  O  G  Z  D  D  D  S  O  F
```

Can you find these words?

AMPHITHEATER	COLOSSEUM	AQUEDUCTS
BUILDINGS	SOLDIERS	CALENDAR
NUMERALS	CONCRETE	CONQUER
CHARIOT	TEMPLES	BRIDGES
APPIAN	CICERO	CAESAR
ARCHES	FORUM	LATIN
ROADS	LIVI	

Timeline of Ancient Roman History

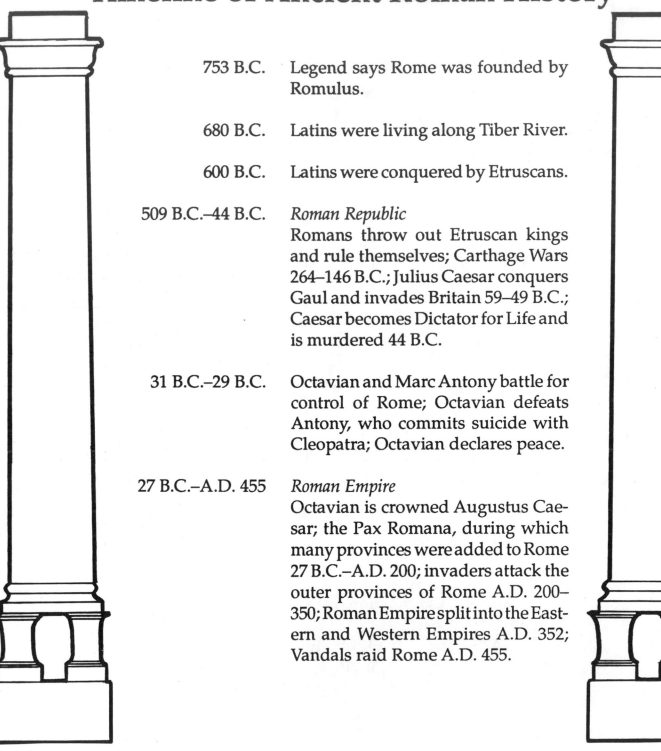

753 B.C.	Legend says Rome was founded by Romulus.
680 B.C.	Latins were living along Tiber River.
600 B.C.	Latins were conquered by Etruscans.
509 B.C.–44 B.C.	*Roman Republic* Romans throw out Etruscan kings and rule themselves; Carthage Wars 264–146 B.C.; Julius Caesar conquers Gaul and invades Britain 59–49 B.C.; Caesar becomes Dictator for Life and is murdered 44 B.C.
31 B.C.–29 B.C.	Octavian and Marc Antony battle for control of Rome; Octavian defeats Antony, who commits suicide with Cleopatra; Octavian declares peace.
27 B.C.–A.D. 455	*Roman Empire* Octavian is crowned Augustus Caesar; the Pax Romana, during which many provinces were added to Rome 27 B.C.–A.D. 200; invaders attack the outer provinces of Rome A.D. 200–350; Roman Empire split into the Eastern and Western Empires A.D. 352; Vandals raid Rome A.D. 455.

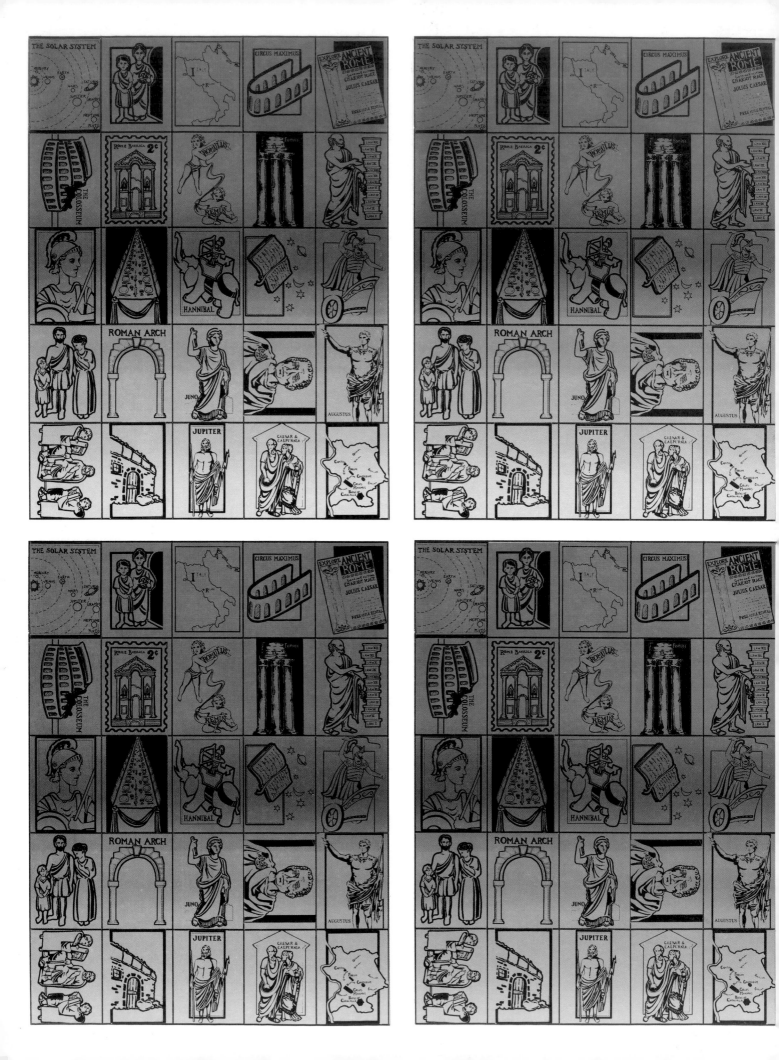